Mercier Press is the oldest independent Irish publishing house and has published books in the fields of history, literature, folklore, music, art, humour, drama, politics, current affairs, law and religion. It was founded in 1944 by John and Mary Feehan.

In the building up of a country few needs are as great as that of a publishing house which would make the people proud of their past, and proud of themselves as a people capable of inspiring and supporting a world of books which was their very own. Mercier Press has tried to be that publishing house. On the occasion of our fiftieth anniversary we thank the many writers and readers who have supported us and contributed to our success.

We face our second half-century with confidence.

MORE
IRISH GHOST
STORIES

PATRICK F. BYRNE

MERCIER PRESS

Mercier Press
PO Box 5, 5 French Church Street, Cork
24 Lower Abbey Street, Dublin 1

© P.F. Byrne 1971

ISBN 0 85342 850 6

18 17 16 15 14 13 12 10 9 8

*To the lovers of ghost stories everywhere, especially
those who told me their own tales.*

Printed in Ireland by Colour Books Ltd.

Contents

Foreword

I was amazed to find that in the few years since the publication of *Irish Ghost Stories* I had accumulated enough material for a second book. Far from exhausting the subject there seems to be an unending stream of tales of the supernatural in Ireland. In this new volume I have included many hitherto unpublished stories such as 'The Ghost Cat of Killakee' which I hit upon by accident.

In a book published recently, *In Search of Ghosts*, James Wentworth Day says, 'certain people alone have the power to see ghosts. They possess extraordinary perception – the sixth sense which enables them to see happenings denied to other people. Horses, dogs and certain other animals have this sixth sense.'

I have never understood why so many people run away in fear when they think they have seen a ghost. It would be much better to stand their ground and find out if it were real or just an allusion. Dr MacLiammoir, an authority on the supernatural says, 'It is generally the non-believer in ghosts who is most subject to fear. The real believer feels no fear.' And – 'Disbelief in ghosts is only comprehensible for atheists or agnostics.'

I wish to thank *Independent Newspapers Ltd* and Mr Brian Quinn, Editor, *Evening Herald,* for permission to use material which has already appeared in the *Evening Herald* Ghosts column. Also, the following for allowing me to use their stories – Dr Micheal MacLiammoir, The

Late Mr Dan Breen, Mr Terry O'Sullivan, Mr Noel Conway, Mr Desmond Rushe, Mr James Maher of Mullinahone, county Tipperary; Mrs Margaret O'Brien of Killakee House, county Dublin; Mr Joseph Hammond, Mr Philip de Burgh O'Brien, Mr Thomas Doran, Mr F. W. Gumley and Mr S. O'F. of Dublin.

In addition, I wish to acknowledge the permission to quote from the following books: *Scholars and Gypsies* by Dr Walter Starkie, ('Don Gypsy and his Blood Brother') by permission of Messrs. John Murray, Publishers, Ltd and the author. *Crowned Harp,* by Nora Robertson by permission of the author and the publishers, Messrs. Allen Figgis. *Gentle Places and Simple Things* by Kevin Danaher, by permission of the author and the Mercier Press.

I would also like to thank my wife for her excellent co-operation and patience in doing most of the typing and helping to put the book together.

Patrick Byrne

CHAPTER 1

Strange Tales of Country Places

According to the Annals of the Four Masters, an earth-quake occured in West Clare in pre-historic times, splitting the land between the Cliffs of Moher on the north and Baltard Cliffs on the south. A subsequent tidal wave engulfed the whole district between the two headlands, and the Atlantic covers what was once fertile land.

One of the many villages said to have been buried with its people in the upheaval was Kilstiveen, and although the others have all been forgotten, it is remembered in folklore and legend among people of West Clare to this day. Many have reported seeing the ghost town of Kilstiveen with its monastery and clustering houses in the clear waters of the bay south of Lahinch and that its appearance signalled death or disaster.

A local resident told me how an old fisherman in the district retailed an experience he had when out at sea. He said:

One fine summer's day when I was a lad of 12 or so, I was out in the fishing boat with my father and two neighbours. The sea was like a duckpond and there wasn't a cloud in the sky. We were all minding our own business when the young man in the stern called out suddenly, 'Kilstiveen! Kilstiveen! Oh God, have mercy on us.'

His eyes were rivetted on something in the depths of the sea and his face was the colour of clay. No one got time to say another word. A mighty wave rose up like a mountain out of that calm sea and bore down on us in deathly silence. I felt my father's strong grip on the collar of my jersey before we were blinded and almost smothered as the wave rolled over the deck and subsided as quickly as it had arisen.

When we could see again, the bay was as calm as it had been before the freak wave hit us, but one of our comrades, Matt was missing from the stern, as if he had never been there. We searched for him for hours, and every boat in the bay was in the search before the day was out, but his body was never recovered.

The rest of us saw nothing that day but the rocks and the seaweed. Matt did. I know it. His sudden prayer to God for mercy was the result of his glimpse of Kilstiveen.

My county Clare informant told me that the fact of the earthquake burying the town and its inhabitants under the sea is easily credible. The sunken aspect of the broken rocky coast between the towering Cliffs of Moher and Baltard show that the sea there could have once been part of the mainland.

*

Another place where a town is said to have disappeared under the water is off the shores of Ballyheigue, county Kerry. There according to T. Crofton Croker, the fishermen used to report seeing the ruined walls of an old chapel beneath them in the water, as they sailed over the clear green sea of a sunny afternoon. Here is the tale:

Flory Cantillon's Funeral

The ancient burial place of the Cantillon family was on an island in Ballyheigue Bay. This island was situated near the shore, and at a remote period was covered by the sea, when the Atlantic made one of its many encroachments on that part of the Kerry coast. The fishermen claimed they often saw the ruined walls of the old chapel beneath them in the water as they sailed on the clear green sea on a sunny afternoon.

The Cantillons were very attached to their ancient burial-place, and this attachment led to the custom, when any member of the family died, of carrying the corpse to the seashore, where the coffin was laid within reach of the tide. By the following morning it had disappeared, being, as was traditionally believed, conveyed away by the ancestors of the deceased to the ancestral tomb beneath the waves.

Conor Crowe, a Clare man, was related to the Cantillons by marriage and didn't believe the story about the burials. On the death of Florence Cantillon he decided to find out if the story about the church under the sea was true, so when he heard the news of Florence's death he set out for Ardfert, where the old man was being mourned by his relations. There was a great crowd at the wake, for Flory was a popular man in his time and all the countryside from Dingle to Tarbert was at the funeral. After the keeners had performed their work the corpse was carried, as was the custom, to Ballyheigue Strand where it was laid on the shore and the prayers for the dead said.

The mourners departed in groups, but Conor Crowe remained behind to see what would happen. He sat down on a large stone and consoled himself by taking sips from his flask of whiskey. It was a lovely moonlight night and he whistled and sang to keep up his spirits.

As the night wore on, he could still see the black coffin on the strand, but not a sound was there but that of the sea. Long past midnight, however, he was brought to his senses by the sound of many voices, which became clearer and clearer, rising above the roll of the sea. He listened carefully and then heard a keen of exquisite sweetness, which rose and fell in keeping with the waves.

The keen grew louder and louder as it approached the beach, and then suddenly died away altogether. As it ended Conor beheld a number of mysterious looking figures emerge from the sea and surround the coffin, which they started to push gently into the water.

'This comes of marrying with the creatures of earth,' said one of the figures, in clear, yet hollow tone. 'Yes,' said another, 'our king would never have commanded his gnawing white-toothed waves to devour the rocky roots of the island cemetery, had not his daughter, Durfulla, been buried there by her mortal husband.'

'But the time will come,' said a third, bending over the coffin.

> *'When mortal eye, our work shall spy*
> *An mortal ear, our dirge shall hear.'*

'Then,' said a fourth, 'our burial of the Cantillons will be at an end for ever.'

As this was spoken the coffin was borne from the beach by a retiring wave, and the company of sea people prepared to follow it, when one of them turned and saw Conor Crowe sitting on the stone, transfixed with fear.

'The time is come,' cried the unearthly being, 'the time is come; a human eye looks on the forms of ocean, a human ear has heard their voices. Farewell to the Cantillons; the sons of the sea are no longer doomed to bury the dust of the earth!'

One after the other turned slowly around, and gazed at Conor Crowe, who remained as if under a spell. Again their funeral song started, and on the next wave they followed the coffin. The coffin and the procession of figures sank over the old churchyard, and never again was any of the dead of the Cantillon family brought to the strand of Ballyheigue for conveyance to their old burial place beneath the waves of the Atlantic.

The Apostles' Wave

Mr Thomas Doran of Artane, Dublin heard the following story from an old Lough Neagh fisherman:

When I was a boy, in company with some companions one winter's evening, we decided to take my father's fishing boat over to Ram's Island. We were about 100 yards from the shore when a big wave washed us back to the edge of the water. We were shivering with the cold and wringing wet. But the determination of youth must have its way.

We attempted to row out on the Lough again. We were about 20 yards out when the same wave swept us in again to the shore. We then decided to tie the boat up and go home. When I got home I was grand and warm. I felt my clothes and they were dry. The same thing happened to the other boys. I decided to tell my father about the strange occurrence.

He said, 'If you had gone out in that boat tonight we would never have seen you alive again. That wave saved your life. I call it the Apostles' Wave. I always pray to the Apostles to protect me and mine.'

'You see they were very poor fishermen like us, and they knew the hardship we endure and understand the frustration and disappointment which is a fisherman's lot. As long as you pray to them, no harm will ever come to you on the Lough. It saved my life too on a few occasions.'

The next morning we were able to skate over to Ram's Island, the ice was so thick. Two days later a man drove a horse and cart over the ice on the Lough to the other side.

Beside the Anner

Mr James Maher of Mullinahone well-known for his books and letters of local lore tells of the following experience:

I used to visit the late Mr Robert H. O'Shea at his beautiful home at Cloran, beside the Anner, and he frequently referred to a family ghost story which had obviously made a deep impression on him. The modern Cloran House is situated close to the site of the ancestral home of the historic family of Shee, and the foundations of the old house are still traceable.

The O'Shea family were sitting around the fire one bright moonlight night when my friend's mother left the room to fetch something from the yard outside. On her return she appeared to be greatly distressed and was pale and trembling.

She declined to give any explanation of what had perturbed her, but preferred to go off to bed immediately. She always refused subsequently to discuss the event of that night, but her family remained very curious to know exactly what had occurred.

When Mrs O'Shea was on her death-bed, her son Robert pressed her to tell of her experience, and finally she agreed to do so. She declared that on entering the yard she observed a troop of soldiers on horseback. They carried swords and appeared to be dressed in some 'old kind of uniform'. She saw them clearly in the moonlight, and in her fright rushed back into the house.

I asked Mr R.H. O'Shea, a very intelligent and well-read gentleman, if he had any theory concerning the incident, and he replied that, presuming the 'ghosts' did sometime appear, he would say that the 'soldiers' were phantom 'Wild Geese' of the Irish Brigade.

Many years later after my friend had himself passed away I read Dr Richard Hayes's book dealing with famous Irishmen in France, wherein it is mentioned that Prince Charles Edward Stuart (Bonnie Prince Charlie), was surrounded at the Battle of Culloden (1746) by a special bodyguard of 130 Irish Brigade men commanded by Captain Robert Shee of the Shees of Cloran and Kilkenny.

The Green Lady

Journalist Noel Conway writes:

I first heard of the Green Lady in an army mess during the war years. A chap from the 4th Motor Squadron, up in Dublin for a match, was firing the old oxen-gun in fine style. 'Come down to Boyle if you really want to stay awake on guard duty – with HER around they don't need an Orderly Officer during the rounds.'

And the lad from the 4th Motors had told us about the Green Lady, 'She's not like any other ghost. You're liable to see her any time of the day or night floating along the beat. I've seen her myself, all dressed in greenery that is so green even her face and hair look green. She just moves towards you and passes you and them comes back again – just as if she was on sentry duty herself.'

His story had caused a tingling excitement among us. Sentry duty in those days of man-power shortage in many battalions was a monotonous going of twenty-four hours on and twenty-four hours off – even a ghost would have been welcome company.

It came back to me years later as I sat in Boyle's Royal Hotel leafing through some old documents about the place with District Justice Sheerin and the hotel's managing director, William McNamara. The District Justice confirmed the soldier's tale. 'The Green Lady is still sought by almost every child who grows up in this town. The children know about her before they even known the alphabet. But Willie, here, can tell you more than I can about her. He owns that old barracks now.'

So it was Willie who told me what he recalled from his childhood. 'The place used to be the private residence of the King family who later built Rockingham House. It then became a military barracks. The story I heard was that one of the servants – for some reason which I cannot remember – locked herself in a top room where vegetables were stored. No amount of coaxing would get her out and she lived on such an amount of greenery, raw, mind you, that she became the colour of a cabbage herself. Then she died and her ghost used come down for an airing in the courtyard. It was powerful stuff to our childish ears, and kiddies around here still enjoy hearing it.'

Until the war the only people of Boyle who would admit to having seen the Green Lady were the older ones. Then came the lads – teenagers most of them – of the 4th Motors. They had no such inhibitions. 'It's the Green Lady, sir... I challenged three times but she just continued advancing and walked right through me.'

– And, in the pubs and cottage kitchens where the people entertained the young soldiers the word went around – the Green Lady was walking again, and she probably still is – to this very day.

The Churchyard Tryst

A quaint story is told in connection with the old churchyard of Eringle Truagh in the Barony of Truagh, county Monaghan. An ancient legend states that the churchyard is haunted by a spirit that only appears to people whose families have been closely associated with the Barony for many years.

It is unusual in that the ghost appears as a lovely girl to a young man, and as a handsome young man to a girl. The apparition was said to appear after a funeral if girl or young man lingered on alone in the graveyard. The apparition extracts a promise from the young person to meet in the churchyard on a certain date, and then vanishes! At this point, of course, he or she, knows that it is the phantom, sinks into despair and sickness as time goes on, and the date of the assignation becomes the day of his or her funeral. The nineteenth-century Irish writers, William Carleton and Samuel Lover both wrote of this ghost.

Carleton wrote a ballad about it entitled 'Sir Turlough and the Churchyard Bride'. The old church was dismantled in 1835 and nothing now remains except two ivy-covered gables. There has been no reported haunting in recent times, but this may be because there are no funerals, and it is most unlikely that a respectable young person would wander on their own around the graveyard.

Haunted Island

There is a haunted island with many Irish links off the coast of Scotland. At certain nights of the year when the moon is full, the phantom war galleys of the Danes or Vikings are seen in shallow water off the White Sands, at the north-east end of Iona, fearsome warriors jumping ashore to give battle and lay waste.

Down the centuries those with 'second sight' have seen these terrifying invaders running swiftly and noiselessly across the sands and along the shore towards the Abbey. Some even claim to have seen the phantoms return to their galleys, to sail away silently and quietly in the moonlight.

As a result of numerous raids in the ninth century, the majority of the surviving monks decided to escape to Ireland and a monastery was built for them at Ceanannus (Kells), county Meath, and they crossed about 814. It was in that monastery the famous Book of Kells, now in Trinity College, was said to have been completed.

A handful of fearless monks stayed on Iona. Traditions has it that the last of these, an abbot and fifteen monks were slaughtered on the White Sands by the Danes on Christmas Eve, 986. Many islanders claim to have seen this re-enacted on various Christmas Eves down the years. Visions have also been seen in Martyr's Bay, where sixty-eight monks were killed in 806, the event that decided the withdrawal of the community.

The southside of the island is said to be evil and uncanny, and strange lights have been seen there at night. St Colmcille left Ireland in 563 in voluntary exile after the bloody battle of Culdremna in 561, for which he felt he was partly reponsible. He succeeded in converting Scotland to Christianity, and became for that country what St Patrick is to Ireland. He died at his monastery of Iona in 597, the same year in which Pope Gregory sent the Roman Missionary to Britain to convert the Pagan English.

CHAPTER 2

In Dublin Old and New

On the night of Saturday, 8 February 1861, one of the worst gales ever recorded sprung up in the Irish Sea, and on the following morning when the inhabitants of what was then called Kingstown (now Dun Laoghaire), went down to the harbour, it was choked with debris and wreckage of all kinds from boats which had foundered, and what was more horrible, dozens of bodies, which were taken ashore and laid out in long pitiable lines on shore.

Among those employed in this work was the crew of the Royal Naval coast guard ship, Ajax, under Captain John McNeill Boyd. Suddenly it was reported that three stricken vessels carrying coal were making for the harbour (the fury of the gale had not abated and snow was also falling). They could not make the harbour mouth, however, and the fierce winds swept them towards the treacherous rocks off the East Pier.

Captain Boyd and his men hurried towards the rocks to see could they save some of the unfortunate men in the ships. As the captain was endeavouring to do so, he found he was encumbered by his great-coat, so he started to take it off. At the same time, however, a huge wave descended over him and his men, and they disappeared. A short while later two of the vessels, the Neptune and Industry, from Whitehaven, were wrecked within 100 yards of each other with great loss of life. The third ship,

The Mary was swept on to Sandymount where it was also wrecked.

The bodies of Captain Boyd and his men were not recovered for several days, and while a life-boat from the Ajax patrolled the waters when calm had returned, a sad sight was seen – the captain's black Newfoundland dog sitting in it. When the body was found Captain Boyd had one of the biggest funerals ever seen in Dublin, with thousands of people walking behind the hearse to St Patrick's. And right behind the coffin walked his dog.

The dog sat beside the coffin as it lay in state in the Cathedral, and followed it to the graveside. When the grave was filled in it lay on top and refused to leave, eventually dying of hunger. Not so long afterwards a statue was erected in the Cathedral by the citizens of Dublin to the memory of the brave Captain Boyd. Since then the figure of a dog has often been seen at night-time sitting at the base of the statue. The last person who reported seeing it was Dean Wilson, who died in 1950.

The inscription on the statue reads: 'Erected by the citizens of Dublin, to the memory of John McNeill Boyd, R.N., Captain, H.M.S. Ajax, born Londonderry, 1812, and lost off the rocks at Kingstown, February 9th, 1861, attempting to save the crew of the Brig, Neptune.'

The 'Dolocher'

Sometime near the end of the eighteenth century women in Dublin reported that on the way home on dark winter evenings they had been attacked by a cloaked figure which looked like a black pig. As the reports multiplied,

21

no woman would go home at night unescorted.

Shortly beforehand a man called Olocher was sentenced to death for an assault on a young woman which resulted in her death, and while awaiting execution was confined in the Black Dog Prison in Cornmarket. On the morning on which he was to be executed, however, he was found dead in his cell, having cut his throat, and the authorities could not understand how he got hold of the weapon.

The following night a sentry at Cook Street steps was found in an unconscious condition. When he revived he was paralyzed on one side, and said he had been attacked by a huge black pig, and then a sentry on night duty at the Black Dog Prison disappeared from his post, and wasn't seen again. His clothes were found draped over his gun, and naturally the story got about that he had been devoured by the black pig, now believed to be the ghost of the dead Olocher.

Sometime later a woman swore before magistrates that she had seen 'The Dolocher' for by now this was what the Dublin people had christened the apparition. For the next two winters the figure appeared at intervals around Christchurch, and hardly anyone would go near that area by night, and residents nearby who kept pigs were a times innocently accused of being the culprits.

After the two years the problem was suddenly and finally solved by a country blacksmith who had come to the city to transact business. Afterwards he joined some friends in a hostelry in Winetavern Street, where they engaged in a long and happy drinking session. On the way home the smith singing in a merry fashion made his way through Christchurch Yard (which then rejoiced in the name 'Hell') when to his amazement he was attacked by a black pig.

Taken unawares the tough smith brought his huge first down on the figure in a hammer blow which stretched the creature on the ground. 'The Dolocher's' identity was then revealed. It was a man dressed in a black pig's skin, and an inquiry resulted in revealing that it was no other than the prison sentry who had mysteriously disappeared. Before he died next day from a fractured skull, he confessed that it was he who had smuggled the knife in to Olocher in prison, and then spread the rumour of the ghostly pig, before taking on the disguise himself, so as to frighten people away, while he went around at night robbing houses.

'Headless Coach'

One of the stories current about the beginning of the present century was that of the 'Headless Coach'. It was not the coach that was headless, of course, but the driver. It was said that anyone who saw it would die, yet it was amazing that many who claimed to see it lived for many years afterwards.

The story of the phantom coach was said to have been first retailed for a certain evil purpose at the beginning of the nineteenth century. At that time the medical schools found it hard to get corpses with 'no questions asked'. These men became known as the 'sack-'em-ups' because, having dug up a newly buried body in a graveyard they put it into a sack and tied the top.

These bodies were put into the back of a coach of the type used at the time for transporting goods. The body-snatchers, naturally, did their work at dead of night, and as they didn't want anyone to catch them, they spread the story of the 'Headless Coach', and made sure that the driver always had his head deep down in his voluminous greatcoat. This kept people in late at night, and made everyone think that every coach they saw or heard in the dark was the phantom one. It also gave rise to the many stories handed down in Dublin and other parts of the country.

In rural parts, particularly in North County Dublin and County Meath the coach was known by its Gaelic name. 'Coiste Bodhar'. In Dublin a place always connected with the 'Headless Coach' was Roper's Rest, situated between the Clanbrassil Street end of the South Circular Road and Blackpitts. In this area once stood the house and lands of Sir Thomas Roper, afterwards Viscount Baltinglass, who died there in 1638 and was buried in St John's Churchyard, Fishamble Street.

About the end of the eighteenth century and the beginning of the nineteenth the area became the haunt of thieves, vagrants and all kinds of evildoers. There were shebeens and many fights broke out. As a result of this respectable people gave it a wide berth, and it is not unlikely that parents spread the story of the coach to keep their young offspring away from the spot at night time. It is also likely that many of the 'sack-'em-up' men inhabited the quarter.

The name, Roper's Rest is preserved in Gaelic on a street sign. It reads – 'Suidhe Ropair, Greenville Avenue.'

Sean Treacy

In his famous book, *My Fight for Irish Freedom,* Dan Breen relates how the ghost of his friend and comrade-in-arms, Sean Treacy appeared to him in the Mater Private Nursing Home in Dublin in 1920. Dan was lying in bed recovering from his wounds after the gun battle with British Irregulars at Fernside, Drumcondra.

Sean Treacy had just been shot by the British in Talbot Street, Dublin. Dan wrote – 'During the days that followed no one breathed a word to me about the Talbot Street fight. I am not given either to superstition or to flights of imagination, and yet I knew beyond any shadow of doubt that Sean Treacy was dead. I saw him standing at the foot of my bed with a radiant smile on his countenance. Towards nightfall Mick Collins came to see me. "Where is Sean?" I asked. Mick averted his eyes and replied, "He's out in the country". Ten days passed before I learned the full story.'

Percy Place

A young English girl who was working in a Dublin hotel and who used to go home from work in the early hours of the morning some years ago asked a friend why there was always a soldier on duty in Percy Place, near Mount Street Bridge. When she was asked what uniform the soldier wore she said she would look more closely the next time. When she did so to her astonishment she saw the figure was wearing the uniform of the Sherwood Foresters. It was only when she reported this back that she heard of the battle of Mount Street Bridge in which many of the soldiers from that regiment lost their lives in 1916.

Another person reported hearing ghostly footsteps behind him as he walked through Percy Place at night time.

'There was no sound in the room except for the clack-clack of a typewriter, which I had put on a folded rug so as not to disturb other members of the family, asleep overhead,' writes S. O'F. of Dublin. 'The time was 3 a.m.; the fire in the grate was dying fast. Another hour, I thought, should see the work completed. I was typing tedious tabular work which was needed for a business meeting in the morning.

'Suddenly, I felt compelled to look over my shoulder. I could have sworn there was someone with me in the room. But there was nobody present, and the door remained closed. I continued typing. About five minutes later I again felt a ghostly presence in the room. This time I went to the door and peered into the dark hallway. There was no one.

'I returned to the typewriter, but the "presence" persisted. Now it seemed to be directly behind me, and I had the uncomfortable feeling that it wanted me to pack up and go to bed. The atmosphere had become distinctly chilly and I was finding it difficult to concentrate. I collected my papers and covered the typewriter. Switching out the light I remember saying, jokingly, 'Well, if you want the room to yourself you are welcome to it!' I decided to wake early in the morning and finish the work.

'I was awakened much sooner than I anticipated – in less than an hour. At three minutes past four o'clock on that morning, Jan. 3, 1941, two German bombs fell on Donore Terrace, South Circular Road, Dublin. There was a terrible tearing, rushing sound as if the world was coming apart. Then a dead silence.

'When I opened my eyes I could see the stars through the now slateless roof. The house was badly damaged, although fortunately no lives were lost. The downstairs room in which I had been typing got the worst of the bombing – it was wrecked. Had I been in it when the explosives fell in the back garden I would almost certainly have been killed. To my ghostly 'visitor' at 3 a.m. I feel I owe my life.

Strange Adventure

The following strange adventure happened to two Dublin friends of mine, whom I will call Mr & Mrs 'X'. Mr 'X' had read an advertisement for a house for sale, and as he was thinking of changing residence he and his wife decided to have a look at it.

It was a dull damp November afternoon as he drove out on the Bray road, and the house wasn't so easy to find – it stood in its own grounds, just off the main road not far from Cabinteely. It was a mid-Victorian residence, with two large windows each side of the halldoor and three somewhat smaller ones upstairs. The doorway itself had some steps leading up to it.

When they got out of the car and walked up the short pathway leading to the house they noticed that an elderly man and a woman dressed in black were standing at the window of the room to the left of the halldoor, and appeared to be deep in conversation. Mr and Mrs 'X' climbed the steps and announced their presence on the large old-fashioned knocker.

The door was opened by the elderly man who had been seen through the window. He greeted them and hearing they were interested in purchasing the house, said he would bring them around it. He first brought them upstairs. In one of the bedrooms jewellery was laid out everywhere – on the mantelpiece, table and dressing-table. There were rings, earrings, necklaces and bangles. On the bed was laid a ball dress of old fashioned design.

'This was my wife's room,' said the man. 'She died many years ago and I wouldn't part with anything belonging to her.' He then led them downstairs, and they were intrigued to find that there was no doorway at the rear of the residence. When they had seen the two front rooms, and were standing in the one in which they had seen the two people talking from outside, noticing no one else about, they asked if he had anyone living with him.

'No,' he answered, 'I have been living on my own since my wife died.' Not wishing to appear inquisitive they then said that they would think over the matter of buying the house and he courteously escorted them to the door. As they were about to leave Mrs 'X' said – 'It must be very lonely on you living here all by yourself.'

The old man smiled and shook his head. 'Not lonely at all,' he said, and then lowering his voice to a whisper, he added – 'you see my wife is always with me. I am in constant communication with her.'

They went slowly back to their car, wondering about the woman in the window, and deciding that this was one house that they definitely would not live in.

Horses' Strange Behaviour

Another friend of mine told of the following strange occurrence in the north county Dublin area, where he lives, a few years back. He lives in a coastal town about a half an hour's journey by car from the city, and he was driving home one night after midnight, when, about a mile from his home, he clearly saw to his right what appeared to be the figure of a person standing.

He didn't worry too much about this, but about a couple of hundred yards further on the same image appeared in his driving mirror. When it happened for the third time after another couple of hundred yards, he immediately stopped his car. Going over to where the figure had appeared to be, however, he could see no trace of anybody. He examined his windscreen and reflector to see if there was any mark on them, but they were perfectly clear. Puzzled, he continued on home and promptly forgot about the matter.

A short while later (it was near Christmas time) he was posting cards in the local post office when his ear caught something the postmistress was saying, 'very strange goings on. The horses are behaving peculiarly every night.' Many people in the area kept horses or ponies, and he discovered that she had been telling how, for some time previously, the animals had been jumping around hysterically in their stalls during the nighttime, whinnying and kicking against the doors.

There were tinkers in the area at the time, and they had been accused of stealing items from houses and gardens, so naturally it was thought they had also been prowling around to try and get their hands on the horses. The tinkers were brought to court for petty larcenies, and when the local Garda Sergeant mentioned the episode of the horses, the itinerants vehemently denied that they had anything to do with it. They were fined and ordered to leave the locality, and they moved out. But the disturbances among the animals continued, and the watching gardai saw nobody near the stables. Then, suddenly, the disturbances ceased and the horses were quiet again.

A few weeks later, said my friend, I heard of the disturbances in Pollgawley House, which was just outside the village. The old couple there were terrified by the sudden activities of what could only be the activities of poltergeists. Objects flew through the air by themselves, glasses rose up off the table and smashed on the ground, and other objects disappeared and turned up in the most unusual places. The old people were also kept awake all night with the most awful noises going on in the house.

Eventually, they had to appeal to Father O'C., the venerable old parish priest. He went to the house and spent the night there carrying out the rite of exorcism. The activities ceased forthwith. My friend again forgot all about the matter, but some weeks afterwards he met a mutual friend and asked, 'How is Father C.? I haven't seen him lately.' 'Did you not hear?' the friend replied, 'he died suddenly two weeks ago.'

A Haunted Pub

A public-house bar in a quiet thoroughfare in a north Dublin Suburb is reputed to be haunted, Mr F.W. Gumley of Glasnevin relates. The ghostly visitant is reputed to take the form of a small, old man wearing a bowler hat and an overcoat. He sits in a corner, near an old fireplace, and he has been seen by odd customers from time to time, persons quite unknown to each other, and all report the same apparition. The present proprietor himself has not seen the ghost, but he tells a strange incident which occured. He had locked up the bar for the night, when he suddenly recollected he had left the day's takings in the till of the register.

Accompanied by his dog, he went down to the bar and unlatched the door, preparatory to entering and switching on the light. The dog ran inside, and in a flash returned to his side with his hair literally standing on end in a state of abject terror.

The proprietor quickly slammed and fastened the door, and accompanied by the terrified dog lost no time in returning to his own quarters. The till remained unemptied till the next morning! He is careful now not to forget anything over-night after that experience. The identity of the old man in the bowler is unknown, but it is conjectured he may have been a former owner.

A Child in the Street

Journalist Noel Conway had a strange experience in the little village of Dundrum, Dublin, near his home. He was out shopping one day. As he walked along the pathway he suddenly found himself walking around someone who wasn't there! It was only after he had completed a circle around an empty space, and was about to apologize for almost bumping into someone that the looked over his shoulder and just saw empty space. He shrugged his shoulders, walked on and forgot the incident. Later, he noticed that when he passed the same spot with his dog, the animal's hair would bristle and he would start growling.

Passing down the street on a subsequent occasion he found himself again side-stepping on exactly the same spot. This time a man who was looking up his shop nearby happened to be watching him.

'You must be one of us,' he said. When Noel didn't answer, not getting the point, he asked, 'Do you believe in ghosts?' Noel, surprised, replied that he did.

'Have you ever seen one?' the man then asked. It appeared that neither of them had, but both were believers.

'I've done the same thing as you did many times, and so have some others around here who'll admit to it.'

They both looked at the spot where he had side-stepped. 'Do you know who you nearly bumped into?' the man asked, adding that he had done the same thing more than fifty years before. It happened to him so often that he mentioned it to his mother, afraid to do so to his father in case he got a clout. And it was from his mother that he got the story.

It happened sometime in the 1870s. A father, mother and a young girl child lived in the house just beside the haunted spot, right on the main thoroughfare.

'They were a happy normal family. Then one night the father came home. Whether he had gone out of his head or had too much drink taken, I don't know. But up he went to the bedroom where the child was asleep, snatched her from the bed and threw her out through the window on to the street below.'

The next day, torn with grief, the mother committed suicide but what happened to the father he didn't know.

'That was the way the mother, God rest her, told it to me. And she used to explain that the ghost of the mother had to stay in the spot where she had killed herself until she had expiated her sin of suicide. The ghost of the child stayed with her mother by choice. And it is the ghost of the child who gets in your way – not everyone's way, of course. She selects people much the same way that an itinerant child would when begging. She gets only in the way of those who might help her.'

That is the story of the Dundrum Ghost as told to me by Noel Conway.

Haunted Lock

A canal lock near Dublin is said to have a sinister reputation. It is Deey Bridge and Lock which marks the end of the level from Blanchardstown. If the tidal lock from the Liffey into Spencer Dock be discounted, it is the thirteenth Lock above Dublin. However, it doesn't look grim or sinister to the person cruising along on holiday, or the rambler out for a walk outside the city.

It is a single lock, with a bridge below, the usual neat lock cottage, and stretching away on the right, the fine woods of Carton Park. However, old Royal Canal boatmen will tell you that it is haunted, and none of them would ever moor there. Nothing would induce them, I am told, to remain at Deey Lock for the night.

Some say that a passenger boat foundered there in the early eighteenth century and many of the passengers were drowned. Others say that a boat carrying a crowd of people making for Dublin to emigrate during the Famine, sank and all drowned. The victims' screams are said to be heard from time to time, and the place has an eerie atmosphere at night. An inscription on the bridge reads, 'Deey Bridge and Lock, 1795.'

CHAPTER 3

The Phantom Cat of Killakee
and Boss Croker's Return

Although I live within six miles of the spot, I must confess that I never heard of the ghost cat of Killakee, county Dublin until the summer of 1968. I had just come back from holidays when it was mentioned to me that a reference to this feline apparition had appeared in the newspapers while I was away. However, apart from one vague reference I could trace nothing definite about it.

Then in the autumn I was invited to the opening of an Art Centre at Killakee House by Mrs Margaret O'Brien. While there I mentioned the cat legend, and to my surprise found that not only was it well-known locally, but Mrs O'Brien and several others had seen the phantom cat since they had moved into the area earlier in the year.

Mrs O'Brien took over Killakee House, which was formerly the Dower House of the Massy family earlier in the year. At that time what had been the old Ballroom was in a bad state of repair, and for reasons which will later appear obvious, the previous owner had the entrance to this part of the building locked for years.

Mrs O'Brien decided the old ballroom would make an ideal exhibition hall and with the help of a couple of local workmen they all set to work to clean, paint and to put the building into good order generally.

On a dark evening in March the local men were working in the ballroom, while the artist, Tom McAssey from

Leighlinbridge, county Carlow, was helping with the work when... well here in his own words is what happened:

Figure at Doorway

'Suddenly one of the two men with me remarked that the door in the old stone hall had opened. Half an hour earlier these men had seen me locking the door and pushing a six inch bolt into its socket.

We stared for seconds into the darkening hall-way. Then I felt compelled to go the outer door. A shadowy figure stood there. For a moment I thought someone was playing a trick. I said, 'Come in. I see you.' A low guttural voice answered: 'You can't see me. Leave this door open.'

The men standing directly behind me heard the voice but both thought it spoke in a foreign language. They ran. A long drawn snore came from the shadow. In a panic I slammed the heavy door. Half-way across the gallery I looked back. The door was again open and a monstrous black cat crouched in the hall its red-flecked amber eyes fixed on me.

I went directly to my room and painted the animal exactly as I had seen it. This painting of an ugly and terrifying animal, with demonic eyes hangs in the hallway to greet visitors who look upon it from the actual spot where it was seen.'

Another painter who exhibits at the centre, the former pole-vault champion, Val McGann from Ballinasloe, who lived in a cottage in the woods of the Massy estate, nearby, also told me that he has seen a cat, about the size of a large dog, on several occasions around that time. He had stalked it with a gun but had never been able to corner it.

Episode of Milk Bottles

Shortly after the apparition in the ballroom Mrs O'Brien got a friend, a priest, to read the rite of exorcism. For a time all was quiet. Then came the strange episode of the milk bottles. As Mrs O'Brien hadn't got a fridge at the time and the weather was warm she arranged with the milkman to leave six bottles in the corner of the yard in an old iron pot which was lying there when they took over.

A little spring ran alongside the pot and it was this kept the milk cool. One morning when she went out to get the milk she found to her astonishment that the caps were missing from the tops of the bottles, although the milk inside was intact. This happened several mornings. At first it was thought that birds had got at them, but strangely enough there was no trace of the caps anywhere and it was unlikely the birds would have flown away with them.

Then Mr O'Brien built a wall around the pot with fire-bricks and placed two or three slates on top. The milkman was instructed to replace the heavy slates when he delivered the milk, which he did, but still the tops were missing. It was then arranged that the milk be left at the doorstep, and after this everything was normal again.

Mrs O'Brien's theory is that after the exorcism the poltergeist was banished from the house and perhaps was an elemental, and so attached itself to the spring outside. It must also have had a sense of humour for if it removed the caps from the milk bottles it left other caps – various head gear of young children were found in odd corners of the yard.

Since then things have been comparatively quiet although a visitor from Cork, a doctor, saw a figure which he described as looking like a hunched-up cripple. (There is a story that the crippled member of a family who at one time lived in the house was buried in the grounds). Another person saw a face at a window when no-one was outside and Mrs O'Brien and her husband, when alone together in the house, have heard what sounded like feet running along the gallery.

The Cat Legend

The cat legend apparently goes back to the eighteenth century and the nefarious activities of the members of the Hellfire Club the ruins of whose headquarters still looks over Dublin City, and Killakee house stands at the bottom of Montpelier Hill, in fact one can climb to the ruins from the rear of the house.

The cat legend is linked with the Massy family and this is evident all over the house. The door knockers are made in the form of a cat's face and stone carvings of cats are to be found in odd places. The house is a weird and lonely place at night, with its large entrance gate leading into a yard where stands a tall tower from which a bell once rang to call the labourers from the fields for their meals.

The following story dealing with the cat legend of the Hellfire Club was told to me by Mr Joseph Hammond of Kinvara Park, Dublin:

One cold and dark winter's night in the eighteenth century a young clergyman, who had been ministering to his flock was making his way home across the lonely hills near Dublin, when he was overtaken by a blinding snowstorm. After fighting his way against it he found himself at the foot of a low hill.

The snow had stopped, and from where he stood he saw what appeared to be a lighted dwelling high above him. Looking forward to even a temporary shelter he hurried up towards it. As he reached the top of the hill he saw the outline of a large lonely house, and as he approached it he could hear the sounds of revelry within. He rapped on the door, and almost immediately the sounds ceased.

The halldoor opened slowly and a strange sight greeted the cleric. Standing inside, looking out at him, were a collection of men dressed in long black cloaks and with horns mounted on their heads. With one voice they shouted, 'Woe unto thee, evil spirit.' To his horror the clergyman realised he had stumbled on a meeting of the notorious Hell Fire Club.

A moment later he was grabbed from behind and the motley crowd hustled him inside to the large dining hall where a devilish banquet was about to take place. He was shoved unceremoniously into an empty chair, and a few moments later one of the members entered bearing a cushion on which reposed a large black cat, also adorned with horns.

The feast proper began and the cat which had been placed in the seat of honour at the head of the table, and obviously represented the Devil himself, was given the first piece of meat, and served milk in a bowl shaped like a human skull. The clergyman, protesting, tried to leave, but was barred and howled down by the assembly.

With a superhuman effort, however, he arose, grabbed the cat, and flung it at a painting of Satan which hung on the wall behind it. The cat struck the wall with a thud, bringing the picture down and scattering broken glass and ornaments around the room.

When the members had recovered from the shock they fell upon the clergyman, tied him up, and appointed a jury of thirteen to try him for attacking their sacred animal. He was naturally found guilty in a mock trial and sentenced to die. Asked had he anything to say, he retaliated by chanting an exorcism, at which the injured cat let out frightening howls.

As the cleric ended his chant, the great chandelier overhead fell with a crash, the candles setting fire to the banquet table. The cat assumed the figure of a horrible fiend, and flew to the ceiling, crashed through the roof, which fell off, and disappeared into the night.

At this the frightened members released the clergyman and begged his forgiveness, swore they would never meet again, and went quietly to their respective homes. Such was the legend of the Hell Fire Club, though in reality it was said that it was a fierce storm which blew the roof off.

The local people said that the spirit of the cairn, from which stones had been used to build the house, would never allow a roof to remain on it, but the owner, Speaker Conolly defied the spirit's power by having an arched roof built in place of the flat one which had blown off. This remained on the building for many years afterwards.

Mr F.W. Gumley of Glasnevin told me that in the early 1930s in order to get the right atmosphere for a story he was writing he decided to visit the Massy estate at nightfall. A friend with a car and another acquaintance accompanied him. He said:

'We drove up the lonely mountain road beyond Rathfarnham and stopped at a wicket gate before a small lodge. We entered the gate, I was going ahead with the torch, and we then entered a narrow pathway bordered with trees and bushes with the old mansion looming somewhere ahead. We had only gone a few paces when I called out a warning to those behind: "Look out! There's a dog ahead."

'It seemed that a black animal the size of a cocker had crossed the path a couple of feet ahead of me at right angles and went soundlessly into the bushes ahead. We hung back for a few moments expecting perhaps for the dog to attack us, after all, we had no right to be there at all.

'However nothing happened, and we finished our scrutiny of the old house which was surrounded by a low wall which presented no difficulty of crossing.

'I was very intrigued by this incident as I had heard the old mansion was haunted and I made quite a number of visits after nightfall invariably accompanied by a friend. About 10 o'clock one winter's night, my friend and I were about to cross the wall when we saw in the moonlight the gleaming eyes of a large cat confronting us; we both got quite a start.

'At the time I thought later it was an actual cat and it may well have been. The confrontation only lasted a moment or two and it seemed the cat sprang off the wall and disappeared into the darkness.

'As a footnote to my recital there was a local legend at the time that the estate was haunted by a black dog, not a cat, but I can state that I saw both.'

One of the most colourful characters in Irish racing circles at the beginning of the century was the American millionaire, 'Boss' Croker, formerly of New York's notorious Tammany Hall. He built himself a chateau-like residence at Sandyford, county Dublin, with 600 acres for his racing stables and stud.

The residence was known as 'Glencairn' – the stables were later taken over by Mr Seamus McGrath, but the house was sold to the British Ambassador to Ireland.

The 'Boss's' greatest achievement while living in Ireland, was when his horse, Orby, won the English Derby in 1907. Bonfires blazed on Derby Night from Sandyford to Stillorgan and the winning owner had seen to it that plenty of drink was provided to all in the neighbourhood to celebrate his victory.

In an article published in the *Evening Herald* in June, 1969, Mr Philip de Burgh-O'Brien tells of strange happenings around Glencairn since Croker's death.

'It is commonly said among the people of the lower Dublin mountains that the ghost of "Boss" Croker is to be seen in and around his former residence, Glencairn. In 1923 a British officer wrote that he had seen the spirit of Mr Croker, as did Mary, a maid in the house two years later. The story persists, so I set out to contact some elderly locals who had known Mr Croker. As none of them wish to be identified I refer to them by their first name.

' "Bartle" worked for the "Boss" at Glencairn and was on very friendly terms with him. I asked him did he ever see him after his death. "I did and all", said Bartle. "Plainly, usually at dusk, and as late as last Christmas. In the old frock coat he used to wear, too; white beard and all, I and the family pray for him for it is plain he is troubled."

'I next asked the oldest man, Patrick, of his experiences. He said: "Mr Croker haunts Glencairn, and several of us, and myself included, have seen him. That is not strange in this country. I have seen others, too, who have passed on. There is something on his soul; he is earthbound, in purgatory. They said wicked things about him in my time, but to us, and to me, he was the perfect gentleman; plenty of money and fine horses he had. I knew his wife well, a quiet lady who never moved much out of the big house. When I saw him it was about two years ago, floating over the ground where the orchid bed used to be. He was wearing the clothes of sixty years ago, and he looked at me, he did. I was not afraid. The dead cannot harm you. When you see them, you pray for them. He was a kind man who liked the humble folk and was good to them."

'I next met Martha, an octogenarian, who was said to be psychic. "Mr Croker was the best of a landowner," she said. "I well remember him coming into my mother's cottage, patting me on the head, saying 'that's a good girl' and heard him talk to my mother. He was a sad man. He spoke of a great sin on his soul. He brought the doctor for us when we needed him, and it never cost us a penny. Don't let me hear you say a word about the "Boss." He has haunted Glencairn ever since I can remember. I have seen him many times.

'Martha continued: "He was dressed old-fashioned. He just glided over the ground there, going in by the side coming from the archway over the entrance, right through the wall; there used to be a door there in the old days before they changed the front." She said he had been seen inside the house very recently. "In one room the climate (temperature) gets very cold when the master is due to appear." She said her late mother told her that Croker was descended from a British officer who had come to Ireland under General Lake, to suppress the Insurrection of 1798. This was Captain Humphrey Croker, 3rd. Foot.

'Research' into the extraordinary personality of "Boss" Croker I found absorbing. Although born in Clonakilty in 1843, his pedigree is entirely English. His father was a squire named Eyre Coote Croker; his mother a Westead, his grandmother an Ainsworth, all of the established Protestant Church. The family emigrated to America in 1845, when the future "Boss" was two years old. After a tempestuous but successful career in American politics he came back to Ireland in 1904 to live at Glencairn, where he was accepted by Irish society. The house and its environs appealed to him greatly. He decided to improve the property, and it is estimated he spent over £ 100,000 – a huge sum at that time.

'The grounds today are owned by the family of the late Joseph McGrath, one of the founders of the Irish Hospitals Sweepstakes. Particular care was spent on landscaping the gardens, one of the attractions being the orchid area. Some fifty years ago there was a mausoleum at the lakeside. It disappeared after Croker's body was transferred to the graveyard at nearby Kilgobbin some years back. This, according to a local informant, the "Boss" resents.

'The "Boss" died on 20 April 1922 in his eightieth year, coronary thrombosis being the cause. Six days later his body was placed in the lakeside mausoleum, within sight of the house. The honarary pallbearers included three of his oldest tenants, as well as Dr Oliver St John Gogarty; the Lord Mayor of Dublin, Alderman Alfred

Byrne and Arthur Griffith, President of Dail Eireann, who himself died shortly afterwards.

' "Many tears were shed," said a contemporary account, "by the humble people who had come to love the strange American gentleman." Today his name is not on the big ornate cross over the grave: looking carefully you will find it on a worn slab which is sinking into the lush grass under the cross.'

CHAPTER 4

A Chilling link with Bloody
Sunday and
The Old Lady with the Limp

Micheal MacLiammoir is one of the most psychic people
I have ever met. He describes in his autobiography *All
for Hecuba* how on the boat returning from America
in the 1930s he suddenly had a premonition about one
of his sisters. Walking around the decks, 'I found that
the present had vanished and I was back in my earliest
youth, and by my side was my sister, Christine, staring
at me with sombre eyes through the tall summer grasses
of a field by the river, or perched in a tree in the garden
at home and whispering through the leaves, "The dead
can come back you know. Oh yes, you'll see one day.
When I die I shall come and tell you wherever you are.
We'll both be grown up then... just wait and see".

'She must be forty now, I remembered, and had been
living for a long while alternately in London, Africa, and
Spain. I had not seen her for ten years, but all that day
she followed me through the boat, singing and laughing,
whispering in my ear, keeping close by my side wherever I went. And by the evening I knew that she was
dead.' When he arrived in Dublin three days later he
learned that his sister had died on the day of his experience on the boat.

He added 'telepathic phenomena and the like can never come as a vast surprise to one who has known such
experiences since childhood with an almost monotonous
regularity. What has puzzled me is that the possibility of

45

these things should be denied by a generation that stumbles daily upon the reflections on the ego's mirror of an undiscovered ocean of life whose froth and spray we have no hesitation in classifying with impressive and fashionable labels, blinding our eyes to the depths beneath.'

Dreaming the Future

Dr MacLiammoir also has a gift for dreaming of future events. When he was in America before the War, he also tells us in his autobiography, he mislaid an article of clothing. That night he dreamt where it was, and when he awoke he immediately went to the spot and there it was. The newspapers got hold of the story and appeared with big banner headlines—

IRISH ACTOR DREAMS THE FUTURE

He also told me of a strange experience he had on the occasion of his first visit to Egypt with the Gate Theatre Company, 'We were visiting the Temple of Karnak at Luxor and I remembered suddenly saying to my partner, Hilton Edwards — "this is the place". It was here in a dream when I was a boy of sixteen that I was surrounded by enemies. It was through that alley that I was taken, and if I was right I knew, we'd twenty years later arrive at the double doors through which I was borne.

'Luckily I had told the whole saga – for it was a saga – to Hilton Edwards, if not at our first meeting ten years before, then certainly very soon after. It was a recurring dream that had come to me again and again during my boyhood, up to the age of twenty-one, when many decisive and vivid dreams constantly recurred. Although at the time in the dream the exact setting was not clear

46

to me, and I had never been to Egypt, I recognized the place beyond all doubt.

'To discover the place of my dream in these surroundings seemed to be momentous. When the dragoman led us to an enormous ruined archway beyond which lay the inner Temples, he pointed to some great spots in the pillars. These are where the double doors were hinged. "But they disappeared centuries ago," he said.

This was as I had dreamed it years before, not once but many times. A sense of something inevitably true lay about me like a cloud all that night. Next day at luncheon, speaking of the Temple though not in connection with my dream, I began to dwell on the extraordinary lasting quality of the colours in the frescoes, and remembered how amazing it was that all had been so perfectly preserved. Hilton stared at me as if he thought I was mad. "But it isn't preserved at all," he said "the whole thing is a gigantic ruin."

'I found it difficult to believe him and it was not until we revisited the ruin next evening that I saw to my unbelieving eyes the truth. The place, gigantic but almost colourless, still unspeakably impressive, it lay before me in a strate of complete ruin, that my eyes had not seen on the previous day. In fact I had imagined – was it imagination? – that I had seen a completely reconstructed Karnak. Dreams have played an enormous part in my life, more than I have ever spoken or written about.'

Figures on the Stairs

He told me the following story one dark winter's evening in his home in Dublin:

'In the early 'thirties Hilton and I were living in a flat

in a large eighteenth century Dublin house in a street not far away from Merrion Square. We knew very little about the owners of the house except that they were a middle-aged married couple, that the husband was Irish and his wife English. They were more than kind to us.

'We had been living there for about eighteen months when one November night Hilton and I were coming home after a particularly late dress rehearsal. I should have said one November morning, for it was between 4 and 5 a.m. It was very dark, and we were exhausted and cold, had not had a drink, and were longing for one, and for the supper-breakfast we knew would be waiting for us. After unlocking the door we were faced with darkness: the lights apparently had failed all over the house. Searching our pockets for matches, we found we had none. 'The lights may be on a different fuse in our room," Hilton said as despondently we climbed the stairs. He, always more full of energy than I, darted ahead, I trudging slowly behind him. Suddenly, as I reached the second floor, the figure of a man came running downstairs and passed me in great panic. I gasped and edged against the wall. I climbed a few more stairs, a second figure rushed down and past me. But it was not until a third man had gone by that I realized with a shock that I had actually seen no-one and heard no-one. How to make that clear I cannot easily explain. But it was then I realized that at least two more men were going past me down the stairs. There were, as far as I can remember – for by now I was in a state of nerves unsteadied by bewilderment – five in all. Although I am not personally afraid of the supernatural, I cried out, "Oh, my God", as the last figure passed for the sense of terror of so terrible a panic had communicated itself to me. Hilton heard my cry and called out of the darkness,

"What is the matter?" At the same time he reached our flat door, opened it and switched on the light.

"Why, you are as white as a ghost," he said.

"A crowd of men rushed past me. I know they are not real."

"You're dreaming," said Hilton. "You're tired. There was no-one. There wasn't. I would have seen them too."

'He stared at me. I stared back at him. It was absurd. I had not seen anyone either. Now that I began slowly to think on what had just happened, on what had indubitably happened, I tried to explain this to him, but it was impossible. "Supper and a glass of wine will fix you up," said Hilton. It did, and after a while I forgot about the matter.'

'About a year later Hilton was away, and one night after my performance at the Gate in a play whose name I have forgotten, I found myself at supper with friends in a restaurant where, when we had eaten, we were joined for coffee by a friend of my companions. He was a doctor, a very charming man whom I had never met before. He had been to the Gate that night and as he drank his coffee he praised the play he had seen and loaded me with compliments about my work, and when our party broke up he suggested that I should go to his home and have a drink with him and his wife.

'When we got into his car we found it would not work. I said, "Where do you live?" and he gave an address somewhere beyond Cabinteely, which at that hour of night and after long hours of work in the theatre gave me pause to think. So, I said: "Why not come to my flat, it is not nearly so far away."

'We got into a taxi, and I leaned over and gave the driver the address, and in no time we were pulling up outside. As we got out, and I mounted the steps and opened the door with my latch key I saw my companion's face suddenly change. We climbed the stairs in silence, and as we reached our sitting room I noticed he seemed not only depressed, but a look of faint alarm had come into his eyes. 'As I poured drinks for us both I couldn't fail to break the deadly silence. "Is there anything wrong?" I asked. I was not accustomed you see to the spectacle of medical men in what seemed the grip of a crise de nerfs.

' "I am puzzled and astonished," he said after a pause, "to know how you and Edwards came to choose this house to live in." This statement, in return, puzzled and astonished me. I did my best to pass it off as a joke.

' "What's wrong with it?" I asked. "Hilton and I both think it is rather charming."

' "Yes, of course. Forgive me," he answered hastily. "I was thinking of the atmosphere. Of course you're a very young chap": (I was in those days) "You probably don't even know what happened in this house. Yet you should, it was only about ten years ago."

' "Ten years ago – I don't know what you are talking about," I said. "What did happen about ten years ago?"

' "Did you even hear," he went on, "of Bloody Sunday?"

' "Of course," I answered.

' "Well,' he said, and his voice was shaking with emotion, "the lead up to it was in this house. Seven British Secret Servicemen. I was on the job. We had to get them out of their beds, some of them, and they raced down the stairs to get away. But we got them, all of them. Oh, the horror of it... I can never forget it. Never, as long as I live. Forgive me. Of course you didn't realize. How could you have known anything about it?"

'I felt perhaps I had known something about it. By an inexplicable chance. But I never said a word to my new friend the doctor about those invisible shadows who raced past me on the night when the lights in the hall had failed.'

Little Old Lady with a Limp

The popular radio personality and newspaper columnist once known as the Night Reporter, Terry O'Sullivan, told me the following story. Here it is in his own words:

'Many years ago I went to live in the right wing of what was then a "big house" called "Boley". It was the property of the rather dramatic late Sir Valentine Grace (in his time a rumbustious actor with the Abbey) and the great ugly Victorian house stood on about ten acres of ground. The entrance pillars of granite still stand and so does the lodge. In the lodge there now lives the foreman of the T.E.K. Dairy, Monkstown, and over the ten acres of gardens and paddocks there is now spread a concrete crust, and on the crust, stands a whole village of smart new houses, where small children play happily in the shadow of "No through way" signs.

'The street signs include names like Abbey Park and Rory O'Connor Park. There is no trace at all of the old house, though there is a fifty-foot eucalyptus tree to mark the site of the lawn. And so a ghost has no home.

'A few days before I went to live there I had a phone call from a senior civil servant who advised me against going to live in this house. For, he said, people he knew had gone to live in the very place I was going to... and they had left in panic the next morning. During their first night there, said this very senior man, their furniture had been helplessly moved and they had heard footsteps on the wooden floor.

'I thanked my caller, didn't believe a word of this, told nobody, and moved in. Nothing happened. Nothing happened, that is, till one night soon after.

'I had a visitor from Kerry, and I suggested he should stay the night. I made him up a comfortable bed in what had been a billiard room, and now made a cathedral-sized drawing room, put on a fire for him big enough to roast an ox, and went to bed. He woke up, urgently, an hour later... "There's something funny going on here," says he. "There is somebody knocking on the door, like this," (and he knocked with his knuckles on the table)... "one two three... one two. And when I open the door, there is nobody there."

'I sat up with the puzzled man for hours, and I did not tell him of my telephone warning. But, nothing happened to me.

'There came then New Year's Eve, and there came to visit me a husky, healthy Tipperary friend of mine, strong as a horse (he was coxing an eight) and fit as a fiddle.

'The night broke both wet and stormy, and I suggested that he might as well stay the night. (Naturally, I had told him nothing of all that has gone before). Again, we made up the bed, the roaring great fire, the comfy look.

'This time I was just washing my teeth before turning in when the big man knocked on the bathroom door and said "I was just lying down in bed when I distinctly heard a voice say: "You are not to sleep here tonight."

'I had to sit up with him all night... and it is important to remember that I had not told him anything of preceding events. At this stage I knew of three separate occurrences, yet nothing had happened to me. I went up to the blacksmith in the village of Kill of the Grange, a dark man called Larkin, and I asked him if he had ever heard anything about the place I was living in being haunted. He was shoeing a horse and worked away as he said, "Of course your place is haunted. There's been a little old lady dressed in black seen walking around there many a time. The little lady walks with a limp."

'From there I went down to the Presbytery in Monkstown, there to see the late Father Dunlea, and I asked him if he knew anything about the house I was living in. "We have been asked up to 'Boley' several times by frightened tenants there, who have heard strange noises and who have their furniture moved around. We have blessed the room that you have been speaking of more than once. There is some unhappy soul in trouble there," said Father Dunlea.

'Soon after, I left "Boley" and the war and life intervened, and I went back to visit the old house one day and found it derelict. Roses I had planted were still struggling to survive, the great eucalyptus tree which had shadowed the disturbed wing where I lived stood up still and rustled its grey-green Australian leaves in loneliness.

Then one day at a business lunch in the Shelbourne, I was put sitting beside Sir Raymond Grace, a journalist too, with the *Irish Times*. And I told him my story. As I went on, he gave up all interest in his food, and when I had finished he said: "But the ghost you have described is a description of my grandmother, Lady Grace. She was a contemporary of King Edward the Seventh and Queen Alexandra. The Queen walked with a limp, and the fashionable society ladies of the time affected a limp too" (Raymond Grace and never before heard of "the ghost").'

'Just after this encounter I went out at dusk and stood

under the great eucalyptus tree which now stands up magnificently in the front garden of a bungalow on Rory O'Connor Park. This is where the little lady in black who walked with with a limp, and who was so troubled, was heard and seen by everybody except me.

'What happens when a ghost has no home to go to? Maybe she still walks the concrete ribbons of Monkstown and Kill of the Grange and the Tel-el-Kebir dairy yard. I hope not. I hope she is at rest.'

CHAPTER 5

'Don Gypsy' And His Blood
Brother and
Other Strange Dreams

This Irish scholar, writer and traveller, Dr Walter Starkie is best known for his books describing his travels on foot with the gypsies in Hungary, Spain and other lands *Raggle-Taggle* and *Spanish Raggle-Taggle*, for example. In his volume of memoirs, *Scholars and Gypsies* he tells how he embarked upon such unusual adventures:

The young Starkie just finished his studies in Trinity College, went to Italy towards the end of the First World War to arrange concerts for the troops there, while at the same time perfecting his knowledge of Italian. On one of his tours he met five Transylvanian gypsies and became very friendly with a man named Farkas.

Starkie got wood from an army stores for them to make fiddles, and they formed a little orchestra and took part in the camp concerts for the troops, Starkie himself playing the gypsy airs on his own violin with them. One day Farkas said he wished Starkie to become his blood-brother.

'The oldest of the group who was obviously the chief explained to me that I had to share my blood with that of my blood-brother,' writes Starkie, 'and I had to give a solemn and sworn promise to join his folk in Hungary and with the tribe. He then made the two of us stand side by side, and taking his knife he cut my hand, and Farkas sucked my blood. After a while he did the same to Farkas, and in my turn I sucked his blood.

'The Chief then gave us salt to rub in the cuts, we broke bread together, Farkas gave me a piece of silver, and I had to give a coin of the same metal to complete the ceremony.'

Later Starkie left that area of Italy and lost sight of Farkas and his four companions. During the next ten years when he was mainly in Dublin teaching at Trinity, whenever the tune, 'Away With the Raggle-Taggle Gypsies' came into his mind he remembered Farkas.

Ten years later, it was on 19 March 1929, Starkie had a curious dream in which he saw Farkas through an arch beckoning to him desperately. 'I tried to rush to his assistance,' he wrote, 'but could not pass through the arch, and I awoke gasping for breath and bathed in a cold sweat, thinking I was dying. I remembered with remorse that I had never fulfilled the oath I had taken exactly ten years before in Italy. I looked at my watch and noted the exact time the reminder had come, and determined to fulfil my promise.

'The story of that journey in 1929 I have told in *Raggle-Taggle* which was published in 1933. I wandered high and low through Hungary and Transylvania, and I mingled with many Gypsy fiddlers and nomadic tribesmen. But I never reached my blood-brother Farkas, or fulfilled my promise, for he had died at Kolozsvar of fever on that very night of 19 March when I had seen him despairingly calling to me. This I learned from a Hungarian fiddler called Rostas whom I met on my travels and who roamed the countryside with me.'

Saw a Murder

A man named Adam Rogers kept a public house at Port-law, county Waterford in the eighteenth century. One night he had a strange blood-curdling dream. He saw two men walking on a mountain not too far away. One was a large man, powerfully built, the other undersized and sickly looking. When they reached a quiet lonely spot on the mountain, Rogers saw the big man spring upon the small one and brutally murder him.

The dream left such an impression on Rogers that he told it to his wife and many of the neighbours, and some time later when out walking with the parish priest he pointed out the spot to him, and related his dream.

Not long afterwards two travellers came to the inn for refreshment. When the publican saw them he was flab-bergasted – for they were the murderer and his victim of the dream! The landlord got into conversation with them and found out that they had met casually on the road. When they had finished their meal Rogers tried to persuade the little man to stay the night at the inn; he was afraid of being laughed at if he told them his dream, but the big tough companion insisted that they continue their journey.

The very next day the little man's mutilated body was found on the very spot in which Rogers had seen the events in his dream. The inn-keeper and his wife were called to identify it. They noticed that the murdered man was wearing the shabby shoes of his companion, and not the new ones he had worn when they saw him alive. This played a big part in tracking down the mur-derer. The inn-keeper often wondered afterwards what would have happened if he had told the murderer his dream beforehand.

The Lady dressed in grey

A Miss Hervey was staying in Tasmania with Lady H. One day she had just come in from horse-riding, and was leaving her room upstairs to have tea with Lady H. when she saw coming up the stairs the figure of her cousin, a nurse in Dublin, to whom she was much attached. She at once recognized the figure, which was dressed in grey, and without waiting to see it disappear, she hurried to Lady H., whom she told what she had seen.

Lady H. laughed at her, but told her to note it down in her diary, which she did. The note ran as follows: 'Saturday, 21 April, 1888, 6 p.m. Vision of (giving her cousins' nickname) on landing in grey dress.' In June news of this cousin's unexpected death reached Miss Hervey in Tasmania. She died in a Dublin hospital from typhus fever on 22 April 1888 at a corresponding time (10 hours difference) to when the vision was seen by Miss Hervey.

The kind of dress worn by the nurses in the hospital was unknown to Miss Hervey, and was found to be of a greyish tone when seen from a little distance. The description she gave in a letter written to a friend immediately after her experience fitted the description of the dress perfectly.

This story was told to W.S. Barrett, who was Professor of Experimental Physics in the Royal College of Science for Ireland from 1873 to 1910.

CHAPTER 6

Haunted Castles

A ghost's appearance in Rathfarnham Castle, Dublin, in the nineteenth century is described in Nora Robertson's book, *Crowned Harp* (Figgis, Dublin.). She writes:

'My mother lived with her eldest sister, Georgina, twenty years her senior, and wife of Edward Blackburne Q.C. of Rathfarnham Castle. Uncle Edward was a dear old man.

'Rathfarnham was a majestic, grim pre-Georgian house, once owned by the Elys, Loftus family. Its ceilings were painted by Angelica Kaufmann; its furniture was period French; its dinner service was silver. Moreover, there was an unnerving ghost, who clanked around with his sword, seeking for his lady love whose bones had been found and removed from the thick walls. Several of my cousins saw him.

'I never slept at the Castle. I think my mother was suspicious that I might hear something "frightening" from the maids. She herself was not psychic, but later she told me of times when her little dog cringed in corners with its hair standing on end. When Aunt Georgina's daughter was married and the family centred there for the festivities, my cousin Hubert described to me the night before, when his bedroom door opened and the unhappy soldier in full eighteenth-century uniform, marched down the steps, crossed the room and left by the opposite door.

'Hubert had subsequently spent a sleepful night, and at dawn he had drifted to the window and beheld — hareing down the avenue — the hired man from Hills' Restaurant making a terrified exit. He had taken nothing of the Castle's contents, or his wedding party pay. He had just seen too much!

'The Castle was afterwards taken over by the Jesuit Fathers and it is now well-known as a Retreat House. It is unlikely that any ghosts now prowl within its walls.'

Stone Wolfhound

Inside the arched gateway of Antrim Castle may be seen the seated figure of a wolfhound. About a hundred years ago this figure was on top of the castle, and could be seen from many miles away. The story of its origin is as follows:

In the spring of 1610 just before the castle was built, Sir Hugh Clotworthy's wife, Lady Marion, went for a walk along the banks of the river which flowed between great forests to Lough Neagh. She gazed out over the lovely scene of the curve of Antrim Bay, enriched by dense woods down to the water's edge.

Suddenly she heard a growl behind her and turning round she saw a wolf about to spring at her, and she immediately fainted with terror. A great wolfhound, however, appeared and sprang to her defence. Coming to, she found it lying wounded by her side and the wolf stretched out dead. She had the injured dog brought to her home and she nursed it back to health. One day after the castle had been built, the hound, to the grief of his mistress, disappeared in the direction of Masserene Abbey, and no trace of it could be found.

Some time later, one stormy winter's evening, when the wind howled around the castle, the loud baying of a wolfhound was heard outside. This awoke the soldiers, who saw the pikes of an army advancing to take the castle. The attacking army, due to the timely warning, was duly repulsed. In the morning it was discovered that the wolfhound which had given the warning had turned to stone! The stone figure was placed on top of the castle, and later when alterations had to be made, it was taken down and placed in its present position. There is a tradition that the name Clotworthy will never be extinct as long as the wolfhound remains there.

Castle Biggs, Kildinan Castle, Ballymoy Castle

Kevin Danaher in *Gentle Places and Simple Things* tells of the following:

Castle Biggs, on Lough Derg, has a frightful spectre, a fire breathing hound with cloven hoof, standing guard over a hidden treasure. The ghost at MacAulliffe's castle near Newmarket, is that of a young bride who was mysteriously spirited away, none knew where, on her wedding night, and that of Carrickogunnel, an evil hag who holds up a light in an endeavour to entice ships on the Shannon to their doom.

In some old war the Barry of Kildinan Castle on the River Bride was betrayed to his enemies by a wandering shoe-pedlar who later paid the penalty of his treachery at the hands of Barry's faithful men. The pedlar was be-headed and his head stuck on a spike over the castle, and ever since then his miserable ghost wanders through the castle ruins...

Ballymoy Castle in Laois is swept by mysterious

beings every Saturday. Castleconnell will fall some day on the wisest man in the whole world, it would be well for budding geniuses to avoid it.

CHAPTER 7

Haunted Battlefields

Having heard that the Battle of Marston Moor (1644) in the English Civil War and Culloden (Scotland) where the Scots cause was lost in 1746 are fought all over again on their anniversaries, I did an investigation to see if any Irish battlefields are haunted, which had some fruitful results.

At Dun an Oir at the southern tip of the Dingle penisula in county Kerry, on 1 October 1580, during the Desmond Rebellion, 806 Spaniards landed and captured the English garrison. Unfortunately, no help arrived from the Irish and the Spaniards were besieged by the English under Lord Grey de Wilton, and forced to surrender unconditionally.

When they had laid down their arms, the English troops cold-bloodedly slaughtered over 600 of them. Ever since on the anniversary of this horrible event people in the vicinity have heard agonising cries in Spanish, and have smelled the horrible stenche of dead bodies.

Mr F.W. Gumley, a regular correspondent to me on ghostly matters tells of two other such stories. The first concerns an ambush which took place in 1920 somewhere on the road between Sligo town and Bundoran, near the townland of Streedagh. On one misty November night in the 1930s a latecomer going home along the stretch of roadway where the ambush took place was horrified to find himself in the middle of a ghostly battle.

In the moonlight he was able to make out the peaks of the R.I.C. caps of the ghostly contestants, accompanied by the clicking of rifle bolts and the panting of excited men. He ran away from the scene in terror.

The other instance concerned an ambush which took place at approximately the same time at Glenwood, Kilkishen, county Clare where a tragic encounter took place in which the R.I.C. were worsted. Years afterwards several people in the neighbourhood claim to have seen and heard the conflict, with the agonizing cries of the wounded on the anniversary of the conflict.

The Battle of Horetown

The Battle of Horetown near New Ross was fought on 20 June 1798, between the Wexfordmen, under Father Philip Roche and the forces of the Crown under the command of Sir John Moore (later of 'Corunna' fame). A Laois resident told me the following story:

'I heard an old man from the Barony of Bargy (he lived about six miles south of Horetown) tell the following incident which happened to his grandmother and his eldest brother. She related the story to him over and over again before her death in 1855 and attributed the death of the eight-year-old boy in great measure to the fright he got on that night in question. He died within a twelve-month.

'The old woman, whom I shall call Mrs Murphy, was a native of little Cullenstown a mile or two north of the scene of the Battle, and was twelve years old in 1798. Her mother, her brother and herself hid in a field of wheat to escape the Hessians (the infamous Hompesch cavalry) the whole morning before and the afternoon

64

during which the battle took place.

'In the year 1848 on 20 June (note the date) she got word in her son's place in Bargy that her brother in the home place in Little Cullenstown had suffered a heart attack and was not expected to live. She was reluctant to leave her daughter-in-law, who was unwell and had two children to mind (one being my narrator). Eventually she was prevailed upon to make the journey in the ass and cart, taking with her for company her eight-year-old grandson. She carried a large crucifix.

'When they arrived in her home place she found her brother out of danger, the doctor declaring that all he needed was a week's rest and to take things easy. Nothing would do her but to set out on the homeward journey at about 10.30 p.m. The boy and herself had only travelled about a mile, when a storm which had been threatening, broke out. The ass was a stubborn creature, and although they both tried to turn it round to go back, once it had got its head towards home it refused to budge and ran away.

'Then above the lashing of the rain and the rattle of the thunder they heard sounds more ominous and witnessed sights which made the young boy cry out in terror and old woman take out and hold up her crucifix and pray for help. First of all, away to the south-west, they heard the roar of guns, the rattle of musketry and the whistling of the bullets. Then came the sound of galloping horses and loud neighing as the chargers drew nearer. Over the hedges and across the road all around them came wave after wave of pikemen, their pikeheads glittering in the dim light. The battle was now joined.

'They could hear the shouts of the combatants as they charged, and the groans of the wounded and dying. At the first charge of the Hessian cavalry the pikemen broke and fell back; then in a counterattack around the Green Road and down to Horetown Cross, the Germans were checked. The boy at the first sight of the ghostly figures cried out and hid his head in the folds of his grandmother's cloak. But the little grey ass with the bit between his teeth kept on his headlong gallop regardless of the clashing figures all around him.

'The stouthearted old woman, with her crucifix held aloft, tried to control the donkey and shield the trembling child at the same time. The "battle" continued all the way by Raheenduff House, over the road to the Cross of Stoneen and down the hill to Goff's Bridge. It was only when the travellers reached the rising ground coming to the next hill that the sound of the ghostly conflict finally died away.

'The Battle of Horetown was a very confused encounter and blunders were made on both sides before the Insurgents retreated in good order. Mrs Murphy lived seven years after her terrible experience, but her grandson was never the same again and died shortly afterwards.

'The Green Road referred to has an eerie reputation to this day, and old people will tell you that the ghost of a Hessian trooper is sometimes seen standing at a large tree near Horestown' Cross, where he is said to be buried. Many of the fallen Croppies are buried in the fields between Raheenduff and Stoneen where the old man thought the spectral combat was fiercest. My narrator, Mrs Murphy's other grandson, died in 1930 at the ripe age of eighty-one.'

Another spot which I was told retains a strange atmosphere is Rineen Hill, near the Lahinch Golf Links, county Clare. There a bloody battle was fought during the War of Independence, in which a handful of the I.R.A. wiped out most of the opposing British forces. Two men who camped on the spot where the corpses of the vanquished were laid out found their tent whipped from around them and all their goods scattered during the night.

Glenmalure, the lonely dark glen where the army of Feagh MacHugh O'Byrne defeated the Queen's Army, under Lord Grey de Wilton in 1580 is also said to be haunted. Campers in the vicinity have seen myriads of moving lights there at night, indicative of a great army getting ready for battle.

It is an eery spot, even in the daylight, and one can sense an unusual atmosphere around one. Perhaps the victims of the battle are still hovering around the spot.

CHAPTER 8

Lake Monsters
Natural or Supernatural

In his Life of Saint Colmcille Adamnan tells us that while on his way to Brude, King of the Picts, the saint met, beside the River Ness, the funeral of a man who had been savaged by the monster from the nearby lake. This (in the sixth century) is the first recorded story of the Loch Ness monster, and possibly of any lake monster in these islands.

The saint told one of his monks to swim across the river and fetch a boat from the other bank. The monster, 'Whose appetite had not so much been sated as whetted for prey, and was still lurking in the depths rushed with gaping mouth and great roaring towards the swimming man. Then Columba, who was watching, raised his hand and drawing the sign of the Cross in the empty air, commanded the savage beast to stop and not touch the man and the beast, as if pulled back with ropes, fled, terrified, up the river to the loch.'

A modern description of the Loch Ness monster, by one who claimed to have seen it, describes it as having a dark-coloured head like the neck of a giraffe as it broke the calm, still surface of the loch and proceeded at a speed across it, leaving a V-shaped ripple behind it.

Scotland is not unique in this respect, however, as stories about lake monsters are common to many parts of Ireland.

Petticoat Loose

On the Knockmealdown Mountains overlooking Clogheen, county Tipperary, there is a big pond, said to be bottomless, which local tradition says is the home of a monster with the quaint name of Petticoat Loose. It has the shape of a horse, with a woman's head, and on its appearance it asks three times – 'When will the day of judgment come?' after which it sinks again to the bottom. Many years ago people from miles around went there on Christmas morning hoping to see the creature. Men going over the hills to Cappoquin to the market with pigs were usually late returning.

One night a man from Clogheen was coming home past the pond. A woman dressed in white suddenly appeared on the cart beside him. The horse jumped around the road and refused to go forward. Next thing horse and cart plunged over the side of the road down the mountain. The man jumped off and had to go home without finding the cart as it was pitch dark.

The next day he came back to the spot where the cart was lost, and there was the cart with not a mark on it, hitched on to the horse perfectly. On another occasion someone coming over the hill saw Clogheen on fire. When he reached it everything was normal and not a trace of flame or smoke.

In his entertaining anthology dedicated to the Fenian chief John O'Mahony, 'Chief of the Comeraghs', James Maher gives another version of the legend of Petticoat Loose – 'known as the Witch of the Knockmealdowns, she is associated with Bay Lough. A delightful folktale tells how an Irish saint directed her to go to Bay Lough by the old road across the Knockmealdowns to the River Blackwater, and stay there and repent of her sins!' The following account of Petticoat Loose was translated by Mr Maher from the Irish of Padraig O Milleadha:

Petticoat Loose was a woman of the Hannigans, and it is Colligan, near Dungarvan, that she lived. There was a poor scholar staying in her house and she 'made up' to him. She herself and the scholar settled on a plan to do away with her husband. One day when there was a flood in the river the scholar asked the man-of-the-house to go down to the stream with him, telling him that there was a very large salmon leaping in it.

The man-of-the-house went with him, and the scholar had a sproong in his hand to tackle the salmon. The man-of-the-house went out to the edge of the stream to try and see the salmon. The scholar came behind him and pushed him out into the pool. He caught hold of a rock that was thrusting up out of the water. There he was, screaming away, while the scholar was trying to push him away with the sproong. A man who was near the place heard him, and going down, in the mêlée, the scholar was drowned and the man-of-the-house saved.

She was dancing one night and her petticoat fell off, and that was the reason she was afterwards called Petticoat Loose. She eventually became a widow, and when entertaining three Kerrymen to ale in her house one day she dropped dead. Soon afterwards she appeared in Currabaha where a party was going on and the merrymakers chased her around the countryside, but failed to catch her. She was also reported to be seen near Cappoquin and Clonmel.

Lough Derg Creature

Some years back anglers fishing the lower stretches of the Shannon reported seeing a blue-black monster in the murky waters around Lough Derg. According to the manager of the Shannon Navigation Office at Killaloe locals as well as tourists claimed to have seen strange objects in the lough. As a result some local boatmen refused to make trips around Crow Island, near Killaloe.

An encounter with the monster was reported by an Arklow businessman, Mr Gerard Kavanagh. He said he saw the monster appear on the surface of the lake while getting his boat ready for the summer months. 'I saw this thing appear in the water about half a mile away. It moved very quickly, leaving a wash in its wake. It was sort of blue-black in colour and quite long.'

A monster was also reported to have been seen in Glendarry Lake, near Achill Sound, county Mayo. A local fisherman told of seeing a fish, about two feet long, with what appeared to be four legs, in a stream leading from the lake. A Dundalk businessman took a photograph of the lake, and when it was developed it showed the scaly back of a pre-historic-like creature rising from the depths. Several local residents stated it was very like what they had seen. One of them reported that the creature had a small head.

A British angler was so frightened by something he had seen in the lake that he left the town. A man in Sraheen, Achill, said a cousin of his reported seeing the monster in the 1920s. At that particular time it was also seen by women cutting turf at the lakeside.

In recent years a young tourist had dismounted from his bicycle and was walking up the rise overlooking the lake when he saw a creature 'Humping himself' along and climbing up a turf bank. 'It was moving in a jumpy way like a kangaroo,' he said. 'It had a head like a sheep and long neck and tail. The hind legs were bigger than the front ones. It was about twelve feet long, much bigger than any horse, and dark in colour.' He added that he jumped on his bike and got away as fast as he could.

The lake which is about four acres in area and has a wooded area on two sides is reputed to be very deep. It is believed there are subterranean tunnels under the lakes. A local fisherman once lowered 450 feet of line into the dark waters without finding bottom.

On one occasion huge webbed footprints were found along the edge of the lake, which were photographed and reproduced in the newspapers, but this was thought to be the work of a local prankster. Two young students camped by the lakeside during the summer of 1968 to try and track down the monster, without success.

What a pity that the only observer who could have studied an Irish lake monster, the young man with the bicycle turned tail and fled. Or he might have discovered that it was an optical illusion.

In Lough Fadda

The existence of a monster in Lough Fadda, near Clifden, county Galway was confirmed by Captain Lionel Leslie, a retired British Army officer and younger brother of Sir Shane Leslie of Glasslough, county Monaghan, who lives in the Highlands of Scotland. He investigated the lake in 1965 and two years later organized an expedition to try and track down the creature.

Captain Leslie is a naturalist and author, and Fellow of the Royal Geographical Society. One of the things he did was to let off five pounds of gelignite near the lakeside. 'Ten seconds later,' he said, 'something broke surface very violently about fifty yards from the shore. There was something there, but the water was broken so violently that it was impossible to see it clearly. When the disturbance ceased there was nothing.'

One of the local people who actually saw the monster was Miss Georgina Carberry of Clifden. She saw the creature more than once, and got a good view of it when boating with three companions. On that occasion she watched it as it moved over a distance of about 150 yards, and she saw clearly that it had two humps, a long neck and a small head. Just as it neared the boat it disappeared.

Unfortunately, Captain Leslie's expedition carried out with Lord Massarene and two divers has not yet produced any concrete evidence of the existence of a Lough Fadda monster.

What the Priests Saw

Three Dublin Priests, doing a spot of may-fly fishing on Lough Ree, two miles north of Athlone, about 60 yards from St Mark's Wood in May 1960 were waiting for the evening rise of trout on a calm clear evening, when they saw a strange creature about 100 yards away It was like a giant conger eel; the head, neck and a coil were above the water and it was moving fast.

'It went down under the water and came up again in the form of a loop', one of the Priests said. 'The length from the end of the coil to the head was about six feet. There were about eighteen inches of hea¹ and neck over the water.'

'The head and neck were narrow in comparison with the coil, which was as thick as a good-sized salmon. It was getting its propulsion from underneath the water and we did not see that part of it.'

They said that they saw it on two occasions, moving in the same direction and close to a spot on the lake off St Mark's Wood. It was in sight long enough for one of them to make a rough sketch of it on the back of an envelope. The water in this part of the lake is said to be 121-feet deep.

When some people scoffed at the story the priests said that they were convinced that what they saw was not a pike or otter, or any other fish or animal, nor was it some inanimate object such as a three branch carried by the current. They were convinced it was a living creature.

In the life of Saint Mochu, who lived in the sixth century it is recorded that the lake 'is infested by a monster which is accustomed to seize and devour swimmers.'

In July, 1961, a Cootehill angler saw at Lough Sheelin in county Cavan 'A large dark creature which remained about a minute on the surface before it glided under the water.'

In 1963, three youths were terrified by something 'eight to ten feet long with two protruding tusks and a hairy head' on Lough Major, county Monaghan. Another local resident reported seeing something similar earlier, and a phenomenon described as a 'water horse' (Each Uisce) has been seen on Lough Derg, county Donegal.

Other lakes which are said to be inhabited by monsters are Lough Mask, Lough Muck, Lough Bran, Lough Dubh, and Loughs Cleevaun and Bray in the Wicklow Hills.

Experts feel that the reported monsters in Irish lakes are plesiosauri, sea reptiles which were thought to have been extinct. They vary in length from about eight to 50 feet.

Glenade Lake Monster

The *Irish Press* had a report from a Patrick McGeoy in December 1969, that a monster flourished in Glenade Lake, in the shadow of the Keelogue Mountains.

Patrick, who lives nearby, knows well the legend of the dreaded 'Dobherchu', which one day in 1722, came out of the lake and ate Grace Connolly, wife to a man named MacLochlinn. The legend, in verse, says:

> *He and his wife Grace Connolly,*
> *Lived there unknown to fame,*
> *Their years in peace until one day*
> *From out the lake there came*
> *What brought a change in all their bliss*
> *Their home and prospects too,*
> *The water fiend, enchanted being,*
> *The dreaded Dobherchu...*

In the field of international folklore the legend has an immortal place and many an industrial knight and scholarly don has visited the spot. In fact, one of Pat's most illustrious callers who wanted to see for himself was Sweden's Crown Prince Gustav. Pat maintains that the monster was seen on the shore by the lake in recent times.

Earlier in 1969, 'Tatler' (Mr Desmond Rushe) had written of Lough Nahooin, near the Clifden estuary:

On the afternoon of 12 February 1968, Mr Albert

Coyne, who works in a local marble factory, took his five children for a walk to the lough. The sun had just set, but the sky was clear and there was good light. Mr Coyne and his children (and later Mrs Coyne) saw a creature with its head and neck about two feet out of the water. It approached within nine yards, opening its mouth and showing white inside.

Mr Coyne saw no trace of any eyes, and whenever the head submerged, the back appeared. He estimated the creature was about twelve feet in length. Mrs Coyne said she too saw no eyes, 'but there were two small protuberances which she took for ears. She did not distinguish any limbs, but the object was 'black, shiny and hairless, like an eel, and had a tail, which was flat and rounded like a mattock.'

As regards the Loch Ness monster here is what Mr David James, a former member of the British Parliament and head of the Loch Ness Phenomena Investigation Bureau has to say: 'Let's get one thing straight. There is no "Loch Ness Monster" which has lived for a few thousand or a million years. That is pure rubbish. What we are investigating is the possibility of a herd, breeding, evolving like any other species in waters such as these, cut off from the sea for 5,000 to 7,000 years.

'One thing is perfectly clear. There is something there. Too many reliable persons have seen too much, with too little possibility for coincidence, connivance or conjuration to pass the entire matter off as only a figment of someone's imagination.' Mr James says that swimming in the depths of Loch Ness, and probably in similar bodies of water all over the world, is some form of marine life not yet known to modern science. He believes that thousands of years ago, during periods of violent upheaval on the earth's surface, fjord-like coastal inlets were cut off from the sea to form vast saltwater lakes. As the ages passed, these lakes gradually changed to freshwater and the life forms trapped in them evolved as the lakes changed.

CHAPTER 9

Two Tales From Folklore

Tim O'Kane and the Corpse

There was a rich farmer's only son in county Leitrim named Tim O'Kane. He was a strong and lively lad, and his father lavished his money on him, so that the youth grew lazy and was more fond of sport and drinking and running after the girls than of work. He never missed a fair, race meeting, or ceili in the area, and it was seldom he was in his bed before the sun came up.

The older he got the wilder he became, and the old people used to shake their heads as he went by and say to one another – 'Sure when his poor father dies, there won't be much land or money left after a year when that young fellow goes through it.'

No matter what he did his father never punished him. . One day, however, the old man heard that the son had got a young girl in the neighbourhood into trouble. In a fierce temper he called his son to him, and said: 'I have tolerated all your goings-on up to this, and have always given you money, never caring what you did with it. Now, however, I am disgusted with you, and unless you marry the girl, not a halfpenny will I leave you. I'll give you until the morning to make up your mind.'

Now although Tim loved the girl in question, he did not want to settle down just yet, and would have preferred to keep on with his drinking, sporting and playing cards. He didn't know what to do, so he decided to take a walk and think it out. He walked out of the house and lit his pipe. The night was bright, the moon being half full. There was not a breath of wind, and it was calm and mild.

He walked for about three hours before realizing how much time had passed. 'I must go back,' he thought, 'it must be nearly 12 o'clock. No sooner had he turned round than he suddenly heard nearby the voices of many people talking, but he couldn't make out what they were saying. Then a couple of yards in front of him he saw a group of little people coming towards him, carrying something big and heavy.

He thought of the fairies and every hair began to stand up on his head. As they came up to him he saw that they were about twenty little men, not one of them more than three feet in height, some of them with grey hair and long white beards. When they were beside him they put down the heavy bundle at his feet, and to his horror he saw that it was a corpse!

He was paralyzed with fear and couldn't say a word when one of the little men came up to him and said, 'Isn't it lucky we met you tonight, Tim O'Kane?' He repeated this twice again, but Tim's tongue felt as if it was stuck to the roof of his mouth.

The little man turned to his companions and said, 'well seeing as how Tim hasn't a word to say we can do with him as we please.' Looking at Tim he said, 'Tim my boy, you're living a bad life, and we can make a slave of you now, and you can't stop us, so there is no need to try. Lift that corpse.'

Tim found enough courage to stammer, 'I won't.' With that all the little men gathered around him and started laughing wickedly. 'Tim O'Kane won't lift the corpse', said the leader to the others. 'Make him lift it.'

At this point Tim tried to run away, but they followed him, and one of them put out his foot and tripped him. With that the whole lot of them caught him, some by the hands and others by the feet, and held him tight, so that he couldn't stir, with his face to the ground.

Six or seven of them lifted the corpse and placed it on his back. The breast was squeezed against Tim's back and shoulders, and the cold clammy hands were round his neck. The little men then stood back from him, and he got up, foaming at the mouth, and cursing, and tried to shake off the corpse. To his horror, the hands had a tight grip on his neck, and the legs were squeezing around his hips, so that no matter what he did, the corpse wouldn't budge.

Tim was terrribly frightened, and started to cry and said, 'It's the bad life I led, that has me in this predicament. I promise to mend my ways, and if I get out of this alive, I'll marry the girl.'

The little man who was the leader then came over. 'Tim,' he said, 'you wouldn't lift the body when I told you to lift it, and you see you were made to lift it. Maybe when you're told to bury it, you won't bury it until you're made to bury it.'

Shivering and weeping Tim replied, 'I'll do anything you like, so long as you take this corpse off my back.'

The little man laughed and said 'you'll be a new man yet Tim before we're finished with you. And if you don't do what I say you'll be a sad man. You must carry this corpse on your back to Teampullshemus, you must bring it with you into the middle of the churchyard, and dig a grave, and put the corpse into it, and fix it so that no one will know the place has been disturbed.'

'But that's not all,' he added, 'Maybe the body won't be allowed to be buried in that churchyard, someone else might be in the grave and wouldn't want to share it with anyone; if you can't bury it in Teampullshemus you must carry on to Carrick-a-Durus, and try the churchyard there, and if it still isn't possible, take it on to Teampul-Ronan; and if you still cannot bury it, well if you go from there to Kill-Breeda you can bury the corpse without hindrance.

'I cannot tell you which one will let you bury it,' he added, 'but one of them will. If you do this work rightly, we will be grateful to you, but if you are slow or lazy, we will punish you accordingly.'

When the little man was finished speaking, all the others laughed and clapped their hands. 'You have until eight hours daybreak,' they all shouted, 'and if you haven't this man buried before sunrise, you certainly will be lost.'

With that some of them gave him a push, and Tim started walking. The night was very dark, and sometimes he fell over stones, at others he knocked his head against a tree, but the crowd of little men made sure he kept moving with his burden.

He did not know how far he had walked when at last one of them cried, 'Stop here!' He stood and they all gathered around him. 'Do you see that group of trees over there', the leader said. 'Teampullshemus is at the other side of them, and you must go in there yourself, for we cannot follow you or go with you. We must stay here. So on with you, and don't be afraid.'

Tim walked on and came to a high wall among the trees. It was broken in places. Soon he came to an old gate which was hanging off its hinges, so he passed through. He followed the little pathway up to the church door, but the big heavy oak door was locked. He tried to push it in without success. He was about to turn away when a voice in his ear said, 'Search for the key on the top of the door or on the wall.'

'Who is that,' shouted the startled Tim. The voice repeated, 'Search for the key on the top of the door.'

'What's that? Who spoke?' said Tim.

'It is I the corpse that spoke to you,' said the voice.

'Can you talk?' asked Tim.

'Now and again,' the corpse replied.

Tim searched for the key and found it on the top of the wall. He was much too frightened to say any more, so he opened the door as quickly as he could and went in with the corpse on his back. It was pitch-dark inside and Tim began to tremble.

'Light the candle,' said the corpse.

Tim fumbled around in the darkness and in one of the windowsills he found some matches and a candlestick. He lit the candles, and soon he could see the eerie interior of the old church. The windows were broken or cracked, the seats were falling apart, and part of the roof had gone. Tim was looking at all this when the corpse whispered into his ear, 'Bury me now, bury me now, take up the spade and turn the ground.'

Tim saw a spade lying beside the altar. He took it up and shoved the blade under a flagstone in the middle of the aisle, and leaning all his weight on the handle, raised the stone. Very quickly he moved three or four more out of their places. The clay underneath was soft and easy to dig, but he had only gone down a few inches when the spade touched something soft. After throwing up a few more shovelfuls he saw another corpse was in the ground.

'I wonder', he thought to himself, 'would it be alright to bury two corpses together?' And he shouted back to the corpse on his back, 'Will you be satisfied if I bury you here?' But there was no answer. Then he thrust the spade into the ground again. There was a fierce roar, and the corpse in the ground rose up and shouted, 'Go away. Go away. Or your's a dead man!' The hair stood up on Tim's head and he nearly fell down in a faint.

After a while when he saw the second corpse lying quietly and saying nothing more, he threw in the clay again, smoothed it over and replaced the flagstone. He went further down the church near the door and started removing some more stones. He began digging again, and this time he uncovered the corpse of an old woman who sat up and said, 'Oh you villain, You villain. Where's the man with no bed?'

This time Tim was not so frightened and drew back. Very soon the old woman lay back and closed her eyes, and Tim then gently replaces the clay and flagstones. He tried again, but only uncovered another man. At this stage he decided there was no solution there, and left the church and despondently sat on a tombstone and started to weep with frustration. He made an effort to loosen the grip of the corpse around his neck, but the more he did the tighter the grip became.

He was just about to sit down again when the cold, horrible lips of the corpse whispered into his ear 'Carrick-a-Durrus'. He remembered then that this was where the little man said he was to go if he didn't get into Teampullshemus.

Getting up he said, 'I don't know the way.' At this the corpse suddenly stretched out his left hand, and pointed out the road he should take. Tim went in that direction and was soon out of the churchyard. He found himself on an old stony road, and again stood not knowing which way to turn. The corpse again stretched out a bony hand and pointed out another road. Tim followed the direction and whenever he came to a road or patch meeting it, the corpse stretched out his fingers, showing him the way.

After traversing many boreens and cross-roads, the corpse suddenly squeezed him tightly, and whispered in his ear, 'Bury me in the burying ground.'

Tim looked up and saw that there was an old burial ground about twenty yards in front of him. When he got close to it, however, he nearly fell down with fright for there were hundreds of ghosts sitting on the wall around it, running among the tombstones, and they were all pointing their long skinny fingers at him. Their lips were opening and shutting, but no sound was coming from them.

He stopped, and as he did the ghosts stopped moving. He suddenly realized that they were trying to stop him from going in to the graveyard. When he moved forward they started off again. This happened several times until he decided to make a retreat. As he did so the corpse whispered, 'Teampull Ronan.'

Almost overcome with exhaustion Tim continued on. The night was pitch-dark, and he stumbled and staggered over the ground. Many times the fell, and was covered in bruises. At last, in front of him he saw the old church, standing in the middle of the graveyard. There were no ghosts visible, and everything was peaceful.

He went in through the gate, but just as he was doing so, he stumbled. Before he could right himself an invisible force seized him by the neck, the hands and the feet, belaboured him with blows, shook him and nearly choked him. He was lifted up and carried more than 100 yards and then thrown down in a ditch, with the corpse still clinging on to him.

Bruised and sore, he staggered up. 'You corpse on my back,' he said, 'shall I go over again to the churchyard?' The corpse didn't answer, so he took that as a sign that he should continue on. As he did so the corpse whispered, 'Imlogue-Fada'.

Again the corpse directed him with its skinny hand, and after travelling a long time, the dead man said, 'There!' In front was a little low wall. It was in the middle of a great wide field, with large stones all over the place.

'Is this Imlogue-Fada?' asked Tim. 'Yes,' said the voice, and the corpse put out his long skinny hand pointing out the way. When he came up to the low wall, a brilliant flash of ligtning went round the wall. On it went faster and faster, until it became a bright ring of flame around the old graveyard. Eventually it became so bright that Tim had to sit down on a stone, as he was dazzled by it.

Tim sat down on a great stone to recover himself. Just as he did so the voice in his ear said, 'Kill-Breeda' and the dead man squeezed him so tightly that he cried out. He rose again, sick, tired and trembling, and walked forward as directed. The night was cold, the road was bad, his load was heavy, the night was pitch-dark and he was nearly worn out and felt he was going to collapse any minute.

Then he suddenly remembered the words of the little man, 'Its the last burying place. I'll be allowed to bury him there.' This gave him renewed strenght and he stumbled on. The first streaks of day were beginning to appear in the east. 'Hurry, hurry,' said the corpse, and Tim made as fast as he could to the graveyard which was a little place on a bare hill ahead of him with only a few graves visible.

He staggered through the large gate, and there was neither sight nor sound of anything. He came to the middle of the ground and started looking around for a spade or shovel to make a grave. He stopped suddenly with a start. Just at his feet was a newly-dug grave. He looked down and at the bottom was a large black coffin. He jumped down and bravely removed the coffin lid, and to his relief found it was empty. He jumped out of the hole and was standing on the brink, when the corpse which had been holding on to him for over eight hours suddenly relaxed his grip, and dropped down straight into the coffin. Tim sank on to his knees and prayed to God for deliverance. He then got down again into the grave and placed the lid on the coffin. Then he filled in the grave, and when it was finished stamped on the clay until it was hard.

The sun was well risen when he had finished, and seeing an old hut nearby he went into it. There was some straw in a corner and he threw himself down on this and slept like a log. When he awoke it was well into the afternoon and he was desperately hungry. He set out and soon arrived in a small village. Finding an inn he ordered a large dinner and found he was about twenty-six miles from his home.

When he had finished eating he ordered a horse and started for home. Everyone wondered where he had been but he told the truth to no-one but his father. He was a changed man from that day. He never drank much again. He gave up gambling, and last, but not least he was never seen out late at night. And shortly afterwards he married Mary the girl he was in love with, and they lived happily ever after.

The White Trout: A Legend of Cong

The story of the above title was written by Samuel Lover in that strange stage-Irish like prose that delighted the 'gintry' of the nineteenth century. It goes as follows: Long ago a beautiful lady lived in a castle overlooking the lake of Cong, county Mayo. She was to marry a king's son, but just before the wedding was due to take place he was murdered and his body thrown into the lake.

As a result the lady pined away with grief and soon died. Not long afterwards a beautiful white trout was seen in the river nearby. No-one would touch the trout on account of its beauty, as the local people looked upon it as something sacred. Then one day an English soldier came along, and hearing about the trout swore he would have it for his supper.

He brought it home and threw it, alive, into the frying-pan. It let a squeal out of it like a human being, but the soldier was a hardened man and it didn't upset him. After a while he turned it round in the pan, but to his amazement there was no sign of cooking on it at all. Puzzled, he kept turning it over and over, but still it remained undone.

Eventually, in exasperation, he decided to taste it. He took up a fork and stuck it into the fish. There was an unmerciful screech and the fish leaped out of the pan and on to the floor. At the same time it turned into a beautiful young lady, dressed in white, with a band of gold in her hair. 'Look where you cut me, you villain,' she said pointing to blood pouring down her arm. 'Couldn't you have left me cool and comfortable in the river where you found me,' she added.

In fear and trembling the soldier got down on his

knees and begged her forgiveness. The lady then told him she was in the river waiting for her true love to come and would he put her back quickly in case she missed him.

The soldier was worrying at the thought of throwing a beautiful lady into the river when to his amazement, she disappeared and there was the little white trout flapping on the ground. He took it up tenderly and carried it to the river and gently dropped it in, and it was away like a flash.

These trout stories are common all over Ireland. Many holy wells are said to be haunted by such trout. There is said to be a well on the border of Lough Gill, Sligo, that some evil person once put on a gridiron. It is said to still have the marks on it. The saints who were in charge of the wells were said to have put the trout there, and only the pious could see them.

The poem 'The Song of Wandering Aengus' by W.B. Yeats was made into a ballet by Dr Micheal Mac-Liammoir and was based on the story mentioned above.